Indian
patterns
to
colour

Illustrated by Nina Hunter and Dinara Mirtalipova
Designed by Emily Beevers
Written by Struan Reid

Colour and contrast

India is a huge country, home to more than a billion people. The incredible variety of landscapes – from the majestic snow-capped Himalayas to the scorching Thar Desert, dry plains and lush green valleys – have inspired artists and designers to make art and crafts covered with intricate and colourful patterns.

People in different parts of India decorate their clothes and jewellery, art and crafts with their own distinctive designs and colours.

Animal and bird patterns appear on everything from textiles to pottery and metalwork.

Elaborate flower and paisley patterns are very popular. This design is taken from a carpet.

This appliqué work was made in Orissa in eastern India. ...

Glittering jewels

India is famous for its wealth of precious stones —
from brilliant blue sapphires and blood-red rubies,
to sparkling diamonds and pearls. For centuries,
these have been used to make fabulous necklaces,
earrings and bangles.

This is a turban ornament,
decorated with dazzling
rubies and emeralds.

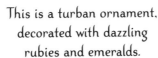

Early designs

In the fertile valley of the Indus River in northern
India, one of the world's oldest civilisations began over
5,000 years ago. The art and design from this time still
influence the artists and craftspeople of India today.

This stone statue was carved more than
5,000 years ago in the Indus Valley. It
was once painted in bright colours.

Traditional clothes

The patterns used on clothes and jewellery can
identify the area or village where they were
made. For example, the Rabari people of
western India wear clothes embroidered with
bright patterns and small mirrors, while
turbans are worn throughout India.

This Rabari man wears a traditional
embroidered jacket and colourful turban.

Gods and goddesses

There are many different religions in India, but most people follow the ancient religion of Hinduism. Hindus worship many gods and spirits, and you can see some here.

Rama, lord of virtue, is usually shown carrying a bow and arrows.

Vishnu, the protector, is one of the most important Hindu gods.

Four-faced Brahma is said to be the creator of the whole universe.

On the right-hand page is Ganesha, elephant god of success and wisdom.

The transport of kings

For hundreds of years, kings and princes used elephants painted in bright colours and dressed in elaborate cloths to carry them in royal processions or to charge into battle. They are still used today for special celebrations.

These elephants would have been painted with intricate patterns in pink, blue and yellow, and dressed in embroidered cloths and heavy gold and silver jewellery.

Their tusks and feet had gold and silver bells and bangles on them.

This *maharajah* (king) and *maharani* (queen) are sitting in a golden *howdah* (chair) under a sun shade.

The *mahout* (driver) sits in front.

Pottery and papier maché

Pots, bowls and dishes made of clay, stone and papier maché are decorated with elaborate flower patterns in bright colours.

Pottery storage jars are decorated in bright blues, greens and yellows.

This elegant coffee pot is made of brass inlaid with silver wire and bright enamel.

This plate was carved from precious pale green jade and set with coloured stones.

This tall flower vase is decorated with white, green, red and blue patterns.

Colour these papier maché dishes in bright red, pink, green and gold leaves and flowers.

For more than 300 years, from 1526, a Muslim dynasty called the Mughals ruled India. They built palaces, mosques and temples with marble floors and patterned walls and screens set with colourful semi-precious stones.

These patterns are based on decorations inside the Taj Mahal. Its dazzling white marble walls and arches were carved with flower patterns inlaid with orange carnelian, golden agate, bright green malachite and deep blue lapis lazuli.

Painted walls

High up in the tree-covered hills of northeastern India, villagers of the Hazaribagh region decorate the walls of their houses with bold patterns known as *Sohrai* paintings. Artists use colours made from natural minerals such as red oxide, white kaolin and black manganese.

Artists paint the patterns onto the walls using brushes made from chewed sticks. Animal and bird designs are popular, as well as trees covered in fruit and flowers.

Mehndi hand patterns

Mehndi is a dark red paste made from the crushed leaves of
a plant called henna. It is used to stain the skin on hands
and feet with delicate, lacy patterns.

The thick henna paste is squeezed
in thin lines onto the hands using
a tube with a very fine hole.

When dry, the paste is
washed off, leaving the
stained patterns on the skin.

Modern designs also include
bright glitter colours in
green, red, blue and gold.

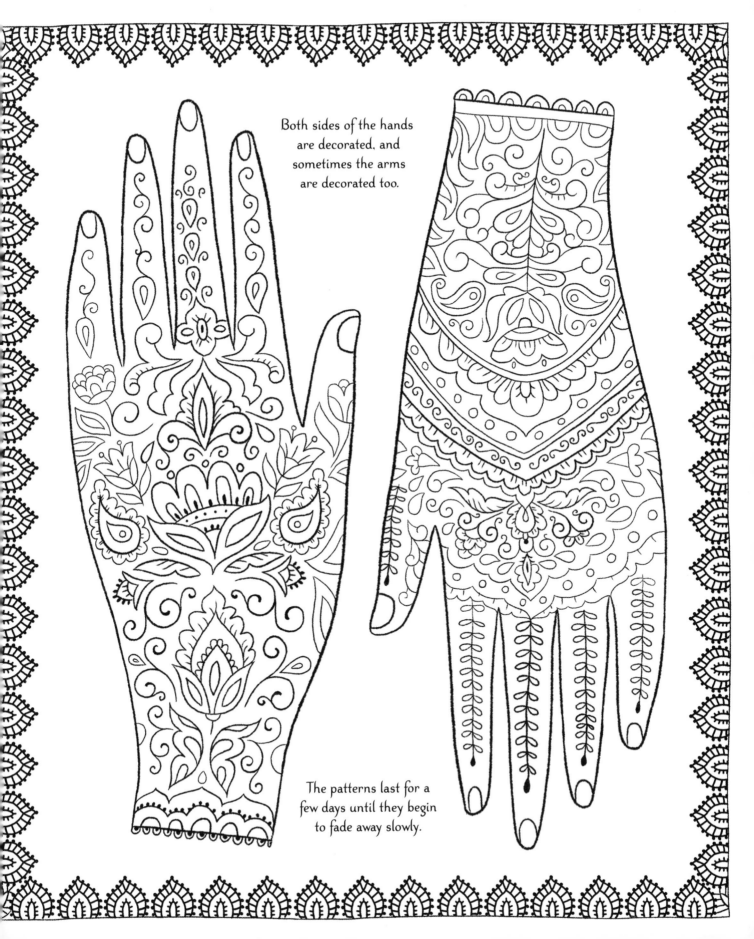

Both sides of the hands are decorated, and sometimes the arms are decorated too.

The patterns last for a few days until they begin to fade away slowly.

Dance and theatre

There are many styles of Indian music and dance. Classical dances evolved from Hindu temple ceremonies. *Kathakali*, from Kerala in southwest India, combines dancing, singing and acting.

Classical dancers wear headdresses and flowing dresses.

Stories are conveyed through delicate hand and leg movements.

Bells on the ankles

His face is painted bright green with black eyes and red mouth.

The Kathakali dancer wears a gold and red headdress and a red, green, yellow and blue costume.

Golden bells and bangles on the ankles

Textiles and carpets

Indian textiles and carpets are made all over India, using lots of different styles and techniques. Some are embroidered or woven in rich patterns, while others are dyed or painted in bright colours.

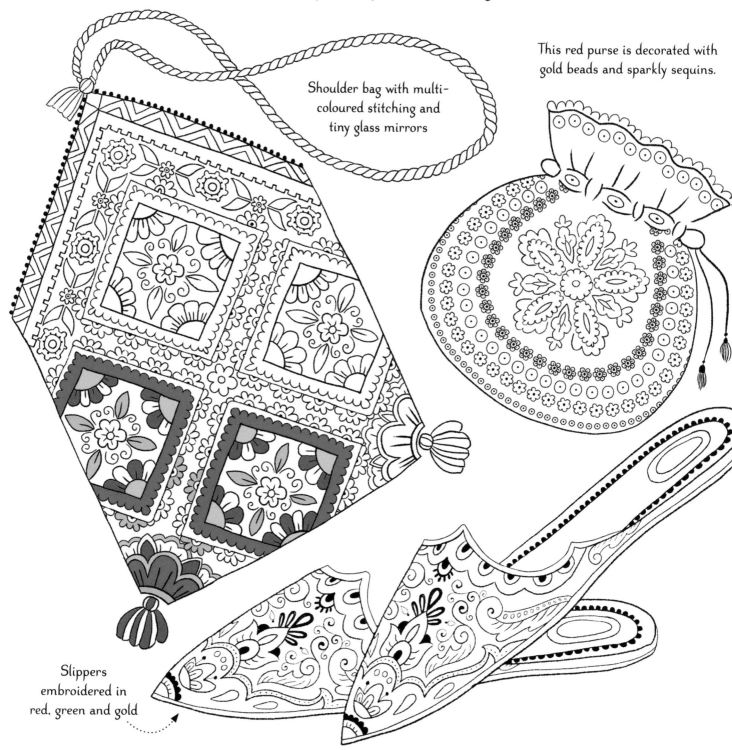

Shoulder bag with multi-coloured stitching and tiny glass mirrors

This red purse is decorated with gold beads and sparkly sequins.

Slippers embroidered in red, green and gold

Colourful costumes

Many people in India wear traditional clothes on special occasions, such as religious festivals and weddings. Women wear long flowing dresses and gold-embroidered veils, while men dress in elaborate tunics and turbans.

The people shown here are wearing their finest wedding outfits. The bride (far left) wears a colourful costume called a *sari*. The groom, next to her, is wearing a long embroidered coat called a *sherwani*.

Dazzling jewels

The most spectacular pieces of Indian jewellery are made from gold and silver with gemstones such as red rubies, green emeralds, golden topazes and lustrous pearls.

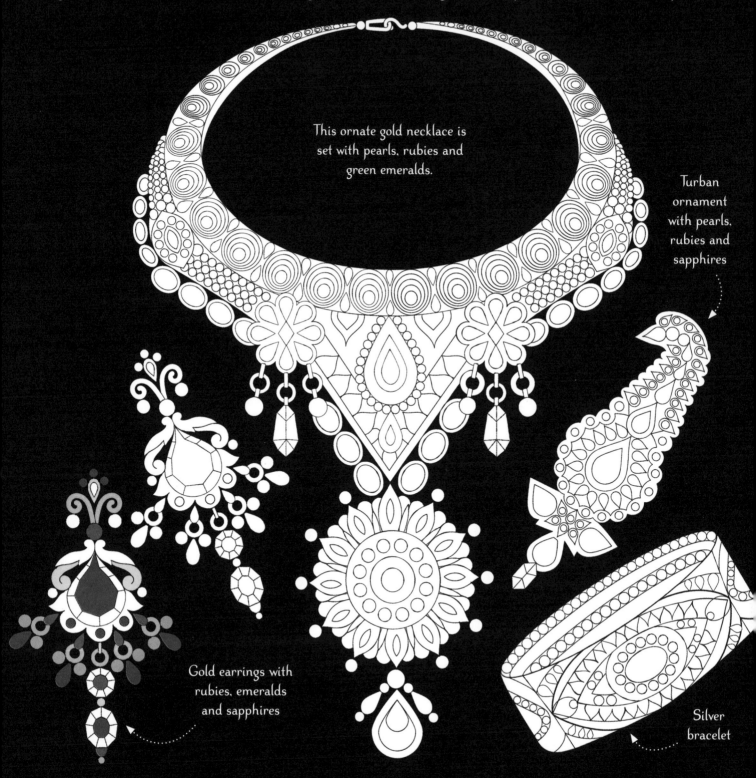

This ornate gold necklace is set with pearls, rubies and green emeralds.

Turban ornament with pearls, rubies and sapphires

Gold earrings with rubies, emeralds and sapphires

Silver bracelet

This prince is dressed from head to toe in colourful gemstones.

He wears pearls and rubies on his turban and around his neck.

Indian patterns

All the patterns on the following pages are based on
designs found on textiles, pottery, paintings, carvings,
buildings and jewellery from all over India.

Usborne Quicklinks
To see examples of Indian patterns, go to www.usborne.com/quicklinks and enter the keywords 'Indian patterns'. Recommended websites are regularly reviewed and the links at Usborne
Quicklinks are updated. However, Usborne Publishing is not responsible and does not accept liability for the content or availability of any website other than its own. We recommend that
children are supervised while on the internet and follow the internet safety guidelines at the Usborne Quicklinks website.